Herman Melville
TYPEE

essay by
Debra Doyle, Ph.D.

Typee

art by Ezra Whiteman
adaptation by H. Miller
cover by Clem Robins

For Classics Illustrated Study Guides
computer recoloring by Twilight Graphics
editor: Madeleine Robins
assistant editor: Gregg Sanderson
design: Scott Friedlander

Classics Illustrated: Typee © Twin Circle Publishing Co.,
a division of Frawley Enterprises; licensed to First Classics, Inc.
All new material and compilation © 1997 by Acclaim Books, Inc.

Dale-Chall R.L.: 8.2

ISBN 1-57840-061-9

Acclaim Books, New York, NY
Printed in the United States

STUDY GUIDE

TYPEE

BY HERMAN MELVILLE
ILLUSTRATED BY EZRA WHITEMAN
ADAPTED BY HARRY MILLER

HERE IS A THRILLING TALE OF TWO ROVING SEAMEN WHO FIND THEMSELVES AT THE MERCY OF A PRIMITIVE TRIBE OF CANNIBALS, PRISONERS OF FATE AND THE SAVAGE TRIBE OF TYPEES IN THE ISLANDS OF THE MARQUESAS.

THE "DOLLY," A BATTERED OLD WHALER, BEARING THE AUTHOR AND IT'S MOTLEY CREW, HAS BEEN POUNDING THE WIDE PACIFIC FOR SIX MONTHS WITHOUT SIGHT OF LAND. . .

SIX MONTHS AT SEA! SIX MONTHS OUT OF SIGHT OF LAND, CRUISING AFTER THE SPERM WHALE BENEATH THE SCORCHING SUN OF THE EQUATOR... THE SKY ABOVE, THE SEA AROUND, AND NOTHING ELSE...

WITH HOPE STILL BEATING IN MY HEART, I ADDRESS MYSELF TO THE POOR, OLD SHIP...

COURAGE, OLD LASS! I HOPE TO SEE YOU SOON WITHIN A BISCUIT'S TOSS OF THE MERRY LAND, RIDING SNUGLY AT ANCHOR IN SOME GREEN CAVE!

MY HOPES WERE BORNE OUT THAT EVENING AFTER MESS...

I'VE GOOD NEWS FOR YOU, M'LADS! NEXT WEEK WE SHAPE OUR COURSE TO THE MARQUESAS ISLANDS!

HOORAY FOR THE MARQUESAS!

THE GOOD NEWS WAS RECEIVED BY THE LAND-SICK MEN WITH UNCONFINED JOY.

AS WE SET OUR COURSE FOR THE MARQUESAS, I FELT AN IRRESISTIBLE CURIOSITY TO SEE THOSE ISLANDS, WHICH THE OLD VOYAGERS HAD SO GLOWINGLY DESCRIBED...

MARQUESAS! WHAT STRANGE VISIONS OF OUTLANDISH THINGS DOES THE VERY NAME SPIRIT UP! CANNIBAL BANQUETS... GROVES OF COCONUTS... TATTOOED CHIEFS AND BAMBOO TEMPLES... HEATHEN RITES AND HUMAN SACRIFICES!

IN THE DAYS THAT IMMEDIATELY FOLLOWED, THE APPEARANCE OF INNUMERABLE SEA FOWL ATTESTED TO THE FACT THAT WE WERE FAST APPROACHING OUR DESTINATION...

SUDDENLY, A CRY FROM ALOFT BROUGHT THE NEWS WE WERE ALL WAITING FOR...

LAND HO! LAND HO!

THE CAPTAIN, DARTING ON DECK, BAWLED LUSTILY FOR HIS SPY-GLASS...

THE MATE, IN STILL LOUDER ACCENTS, HAILED THE MASTHEAD...

WHERE-AWAY?

THE COOK THRUST HIS HEAD OUT OF THE GALLEY...

EVEN BOATSWAIN, THE DOG, LEAPED UP AND BARKED MOST FURIOUSLY...

LAND HO! AY, THERE IT WAS! A HARDLY PERCEPTIBLE, BLUE, IRREGULAR OUTLINE, INDICATING THE BOLD CONTOUR OF THE LOFTY HEIGHTS OF NUKAHIVA, THE PRINCIPAL ISLAND OF THE MARQUESAS...

SEVERAL HOURS LATER, NUKAHIVA LOOMED UP IN THE DISTANCE...

TOWARD NOON, WE SLOWLY ENTERED THE LOVELY HARBOR, AND WERE SURPRISED TO SEE FRENCH MEN-O-WAR RIDING AT ANCHOR...

LATER WE LEARNED THAT THE GROUP OF ISLANDS HAD JUST BEEN TAKEN POSSESSION OF BY REAR ADMIRAL DU PETIT THOUARS OF THE FRENCH NAVY...

AS WE ADVANCED UP THE BAY, NUMEROUS CANOES PUSHED OFF FROM THE SURROUNDING SHORES, THEIR SAVAGE OCCUPANTS STRUGGLING TO GET ABOARD OF US...

SUDDENLY, OUR ATTENTION WAS DRAWN TO WHAT LOOKED LIKE A SHOAL OF FISH SPORTING ON THE SURFACE.

WHINENIES! WHINENIES!

OUR SAVAGE FRIENDS ASSURED US THAT THE COMMOTION WAS CAUSED BY WHINENIES' WHO WERE COMING OFF FROM THE SHORE TO WELCOME US...

'NATIVE GIRLS'

AS THEY DREW NEARER, I ALMOST FANCIED THEY COULD BE NOTHING ELSE THAN SO MANY MERMAIDS... AND VERY LIKE MERMAIDS THEY BEHAVED TOO...

AS WE SAILED INTO THE MIDST OF THESE SWIMMING NYMPHS, THEY BOARDED US AT EVERY QUARTER...

MANY, SEIZING HOLD OF THE CHAIN PLATES, SPRANG INTO THE CHAINS... OTHERS, CATCHING AT THE BOB STAYS, WREATHED THEIR SLENDER FORMS ABOUT THE ROPE...

THE "DOLLY" WAS FAIRLY CAPTURED BY THE FAIR INVADERS, AND NEVER, I WILL SAY, WAS A VESSEL CARRIED BEFORE SUCH A PARTY OF DASHING AND IRRESISTIBLE BOARDERS...

OUR SHIP HAD NOT BEEN MANY DAYS IN THE HARBOR OF NUKAHIVA, BEFORE I CAME TO THE DETERMINATION OF LEAVING HER. I WAS READY TO RISK UNKNOWN HARDSHIPS AMONG THE NATIVES RATHER THAN CHANCE MANY MORE MONTHS OF THE OPEN SEA AT THE MERCY OF A CRUEL AND ABUSIVE CAPTAIN...

I PROCEEDED TO ACQUIRE ALL THE INFORMATION I COULD OBTAIN RELATING TO THE ISLANDS AND ITS INHABITANTS WITH A VIEW OF SHAPING PLANS TO ESCAPE.

I LEARNED THAT THE NATIVES OF HAPPAR CHERISHED THE MOST FRIENDLY RELATIONS WITH THE INHABITANTS OF NUKAHIVA. ON THE OTHER SIDE OF HAPPAR WAS THE MAGNIFICENT VALLEY OF THE DREADED TYPEES, FEARED BY BOTH TRIBES...

TYPEE

HAPPAR

NUKUHIVA

ONE NIGHT, I PERCEIVED ONE OF THE SHIP'S COMPANY LEANING OVER THE BULWARKS, APPARENTLY PLUNGED IN A PROFOUND REVERIE. I HESITATED A MOMENT, AND THEN APPROACHED HIM.

"I SAY, TOBY; YOU CERTAINLY LOOK DOWN IN THE MOUTH TONIGHT!"

"WHY WOULDN'T I BE, WHEN I THINK WE'LL SOON BE SHOVIN' OFF IN THIS RAT HOLE!"

"HERE WE ARE, IMPRISONED IN THIS WORMY OLD TUB, SURROUNDED ON ALL SIDES BY AN UNTOUCHABLE GARDEN OF EDEN!"

I LOST NO TIME IN CONFIDING MY PLANS TO TOBY AND INVITED HIM TO JOIN ME IN MY ESCAPE...

"YOU KNOW WE WOULD BE RISKING OUR SKINS IF WE WERE TO FALL IN WITH SOME OF THOSE MAN-EATING SAVAGES!"

"MANY OF THESE NATIVES ARE FRIENDLY, TOBY! IT'S THE TYPEES WE HAVE MOST TO FEAR! IF WE CAN GET INTO THOSE HILLS FOR A WEEK OR TWO, THE CAPTAIN'D NEVER FIND US, AND WE COULD HIDE IN THE RIDGES UNTIL THE SHIP SAILS!"

A FEW WORDS SUFFICED FOR A MUTUAL UNDERSTANDING, AND TO ELUDE SUSPICION, EACH REPAIRED TO HIS HAMMOCK...

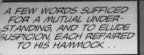

WE WERE TO BE SENT ASHORE THE NEXT MORNING WITH THE STARBOARD WATCH. OUR PLAN WAS TO SEPARATE FROM THE REST OF THE MEN AND STRIKE AT ONCE FOR THE MOUNTAINS...

EARLY NEXT MORNING...

ALL RIGHT, MEN, YOU'RE DETERMINED TO HAVE YOUR LIBERTY ASHORE AND YOU'LL GET IT! BUT MARK YOU WELL. KEEP OUT OF THE WAY OF THOSE ACCURSED HEATHENS IF YOU DON'T WANT TO SPEND YOUR LAST DAY ON EARTH IN A BLOODY SOUP POT!

IF WHAT THE CAPTAIN SAYS IS TRUE, WE MAY BE IN FOR A LOT OF TROUBLE ASHORE!

HE CAN'T BOUNCE ME OUT OF MY LIBERTY! I'D GO ASHORE IF THE CANNIBALS STOOD READY TO BROIL ME ON LAND!

TOBY AND I COMPLETED ARRANGEMENTS...

ALL SET, TOBY! THE BOAT'S LEAVING AT TWO BELLS.

IT CAN'T LEAVE TOO SOON TO SUIT ME!

LATER, AS WE PULLED AWAY, THE HEAVENS OPENED UP AND THE RAIN CAME DOWN IN TORRENTS.

WE FLED FOR SHELTER UNDER COVER OF AN IMMENSE CANOE HOUSE WHICH STOOD HARD BY THE BEACH...

IT MIGHT BE A GOOD IDEA TO HEAD FOR THAT CANOE HOUSE TILL THE STORM LETS UP!

THE MONOTONOUS BEATING OF THE RAIN OVERHEAD BEGAN TO EXACT A DROWSY INFLUENCE UPON THE MEN, WHO SOON FELL ASLEEP...

NOW'S OUR CHANCE, TOBY! LET'S GO!

THE HEAVY RAIN FAVORED OUR ENTERPRISE, AS IT DROVE THE ISLANDERS INTO THEIR HOUSES, CLEARING THE WAY FOR OUR CLIMB TO THE RIDGES...

DRENCHED TO THE SKIN, WE MADE OUR WAY THROUGH SOME EXTENSIVE THICKETS TO AVOID MEETING THE NATIVES...

NOW, TOBY, NOT A WORD OR A GLANCE BACKWARD TILL WE STAND ON THE SUMMIT OF YONDER MOUNTAIN! YOU ARE THE NIMBLER, SO LEAD ON AND I WILL FOLLOW!

ALL RIGHT, BROTHER! QUICK'S OUR PLAY. ONLY LET'S KEEP CLOSE TOGETHER, THAT'S ALL!

WE WERE SOON STOPPED BY A MASS OF TALL YELLOW REEDS, AS TOUGH AND STUBBORN AS SO MANY RODS OF STEEL...

WE'LL NEVER MAKE THE RIDGE THROUGH THAT JUNGLE OF REEDS!

I'LL GO FIRST THIS TIME, TOBY! I'LL HAVE A BETTER CHANCE OF BREAKING THROUGH WITH MY HEAVIER WEIGHT!

AT THE RISK OF BREAKING OUR NECKS, WE PROCEEDED TO LOWER OURSELVES BY THE TANGLED ROOTS WHICH CLUSTERED ABOUT ALL THE CREVICES OF THE ROCK...

WE LANDED SAFELY AT THE BOTTOM...

FOR ONCE, OUR TRAINING BEFORE THE MAST BRINGS ITS JUST REWARDS!

THE SIGHT THAT NOW GREETED US WAS ONE THAT WILL EVER BE VIVIDLY IMPRESSED UPON MY MIND...

MAN ALIVE, TOBY! DID YOU EVER SEE ANYTHING SO MAGNIFICENT?

I DARE SAY, I'D APPRECIATE IT MORE IF I COULD TAKE A LONG DRAUGHT OUT OF ONE OF THOSE STREAMS!

WE SPENT A NIGHT OF HORROR UNDER A CRUDE HUT, WHICH WE BUILT WITH THE LIMBS OF TREES AND COVERED WITH A SPECIES OF BROAD-BLADED GRASS THAT GREW IN EVERY CRACK IN THE RAVINE...

NEXT MORNING, WE PARTOOK OF OUR MEAGRE RATIONS, AND CONTINUED ON OUR WEARY WAY. SEVERAL HOURS LATER, BESET BY A BURNING FEVER BROUGHT ON BY OUR DAMPENED CONDITION, WE FLUNG OURSELVES ON THE WET GROUND AND MY COMPANION WENT PROMPTLY TO SLEEP...

CHANCING TO PUSH ASIDE A BRANCH, MY EYE CAUGHT A SIGHT WHICH BROUGHT ME QUICKLY TO MY FEET...

TOBY! TOBY! LOOK... THE VALLEY... RIGHT BEFORE OUR VERY FEET!

BEFORE OUR EYES, SWEEPING AWAY IN LONG WAVES, LAY THE VALLEY BELOW, BESET ON BOTH SIDES WITH GRASSY CLIFFS AND TALL PRECIPICES. HALF WAY DOWN, WE COULD SEE THE PALMETTO THATCHED HOUSES OF THE NATIVES...

COMES NOW THE BURNING QUESTION... IS IT THE VALLEY OF THE FRIENDLY HAPPARS OR THE HOMES OF THE MAN-EATING TYPEES?

WE HAVE OUR CHOICE BETWEEN STARVING TO DEATH OR MAKING OUR DESCENT AND HOPING FOR THE BEST!

AFTER FIVE DAYS OF GREAT TOIL AND UNTOLD DANGERS, WE ARRIVED IN THE VALLEY AND PUSHED STEADILY ONWARD...

LOOK, TOBY! ISN'T THAT A FRUIT TREE?

GREAT SCOTT! MANNA FROM HEAVEN!

SUDDENLY. . .

COME QUICK, BROTHER! LOOK WHAT WE HAVE HERE!

THEY'VE PROBABLY SEEN US AND ARE HIDING AWAY!

TYPEE OR HAPPAR? NOW'S THE TIME TO FIND OUT, TOBY!

QUICKLY, WE IMPROVISED TWO FLAGS OF TRUCE AND APPROACHED THE SHRINKING NATIVES. . .

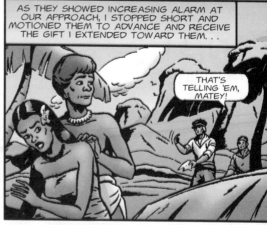

AS THEY SHOWED INCREASING ALARM AT OUR APPROACH, I STOPPED SHORT AND MOTIONED THEM TO ADVANCE AND RECEIVE THE GIFT I EXTENDED TOWARD THEM. . .

THAT'S TELLING 'EM, MATEY!

IT'S BLESSED TO GIVE, SAYS I!

IT'LL BE NO BLESSING IF THEY TURN OUT TO BE TYPEES, OLD BOY!

REASSURED BY OUR DISPLAY OF FRIENDSHIP, THEY MOTIONED TO US TO FOLLOW THEM. . .

WE'LL FIND OUT SOON ENOUGH NOW!

ONE OF THE CHIEFS, WHO APPEARED TO BE HIGHEST IN RANK, PLACED HIMSELF DIRECTLY FACING ME AND STARED FEROCIOUSLY AT ME...

HOPING TO WIN HIM OVER TO MY GOOD GRACES, I OFFERED HIM A HANDFUL OF MY TOBACCO...

HE QUIETLY REJECTED THE PROFERRED GIFT AND MOTIONED ME TO RETURN IT TO ITS PLACE...

WAS THE ACTION OF THE CHIEF A TOKEN OF ENMITY? TYPEE OR HAPPAR? I STARTED, FOR AT THAT MOMENT, THE CHIEF REPEATED THE IDENTICAL QUESTION...

TYPEE...
HAPPAR?

I PAUSED FOR A MOMENT, AND I KNOW NOT BY WHAT IMPULSE I ANSWERED...

TYPEE! TYPEE MORTARKEE! *

* TYPEE GOOD

TYPEE MORTAR-KEE! TYPEE MORTARKEE!

THE COMMOTION HAVING SUBSIDED, THE CHIEF LAID HIS HAND ON HIS BREAST AND INTRODUCED HIMSELF . . .

MEHEVI! MEHEVI!

SUSPECTING THAT MY OWN NAME WOULD BE TOO UNPRONOUNCEABLE FOR HIM, I INTRODUCED MYSELF AS TOM AND MY COMPANION, TOBY . . .

TOMMO! TOBY!

TOMMO, TOBY, HUNGRY!

NOW YOU'RE TALKING, MATEY! I'M SO HUNGRY I COULD DO JUSTICE TO A BOWL-FUL OF FRIED SEAWEED!

AT THE CHIEF'S SIGNAL, ONE OF THE NATIVES BROUGHT IN A DISH OF POEEPOEE *, AND TWO OPENED COCONUTS . . .

* A NATIVE DISH MADE FROM BREAD-FRUIT

WE DRAINED THE GOBLETS OF THEIR REFRESHING DRAUGHTS. . .

THE DISHES OF POEE-POEE WERE THEN PLACED BEFORE US. THIS IS A FAVORITE FOOD OF MARQUESANS AND IS MANUFACTURED FROM THE PRODUCT OF THE BREAD-FRUIT TREE. IT SOMEWHAT RESEMBLES, IN ITS PLASTIC NATURE, A THICK PASTE, AND IS SOMEWHAT TART TO THE TASTE . . .

CONFRONTED WITH THE POEE-POEE, WE PAUSED TO CONSIDER IN WHAT MANNER WE WERE TO BRING THE FOOD TO OUR MOUTHS . . .

FINE TYPEEAN HOSPITAL-ITY, I CALLS IT! THEY SERVE US A POT OF GLUE AND NOT EVEN A SPOON TO EAT IT WITH!

JUST WATCH ME, TOBY! IT'S AS EASY AS. . .

OH, OH! LOOKS LIKE I STILL HAVE TO LEARN THE TECHNIQUE OF EATING POEE-POEE!

YOU'VE SURE MADE A MESS OF THINGS, OLD MAN!

BEHIND HIS MAGNIFICENT WAR DRESS, I RECOGNIZED THE CHIEF WHO HAD QUESTIONED US THE NIGHT BEFORE . . .

IT'S THE BIG CHIEF MEHEVI, HIMSELF!

JUDGING FROM HIS COSTUME, I'M AFRAID IT'S NOT A PEACEFUL MISSION HE'S ON!

APPROACHING US, HE ENDEAVORED TO MAKE US UNDERSTAND THAT HIS ATTITUDE TOWARD US WAS FRIENDLY . . .

NOTICING MY SWOLLEN LIMB, HE EXAMINED IT WITH THE UTMOST ATTENTION . . .

THEN, CLAPPING HIS HANDS . . .

I HOPE IT'S NOT THE MEDICINE MAN HE'S SENDING FOR!

MOST PROBABLY THE BUTCHER! THE WAY HE EXAMINED YOUR LEG, HE MUST THINK IT'LL MAKE A FINE SOUP BONE FOR DINNER!

IN A FEW MOMENTS, AN AGED ISLANDER ENTERED . . .

WELL, IF IT ISN'T OLD HIPPOCRATES' HIMSELF!

I SHUDDER TO THINK OF WHAT HE'LL DO TO MY LEG!

' GREEK "FATHER OF MEDICINE"

MEHEVI UNCOVERD THE INJURED MEMBER AND SHOWED IT TO THE NEW-COMER . . .

HE IMMEDIATELY WENT TO WORK ON IT, PINCHING AND HAMMERING IT, TILL I ROARED WITH PAIN . . .

OW! WOW!

TOBY PLEADED IN VAIN WITH THE CHIEF . . .

COME ON, MEHEVI, CALL THAT WITCH-DOCTOR OFF!

WAVING TOBY ASIDE, MEHEVI HELD ME IN HIS POW-ERFUL GRIP. WHILE HE ACTUALLY ENCOURAGED THE WRETCH . . .

MORTARKEE, TOMMO! MORTARKEE, TOMMO!

WORN OUT WITH HIS EXERTIONS, MY TORMENTOR NOW APPLIED SOME MOISTENED HERBS TO THE INFLAMED PARTS. . .

OH, MY POOR LEG! I'LL NEVER BE ABLE TO USE IT AGAIN!

THE OLD TORTURER! I'D LIKE TO GIVE HIM A DOSE OF HIS OWN MEDICINE!

AFTER A CONFIDENTIAL CHAT WITH SOME IMAGINARY DEMONS, MY PHYSICIAN TOOK HIS DEPARTURE. . .

WHILE TOBY WAS LEFT TO HIS OWN RESOURCES, KORY-KORY INSISTED ON FEEDING ME, DESPITE MY STRONG OBJECTIONS . . .

NO, NO, KORY-KORY! TOMMO FEED SELF!

I WOULDN'T CARRY ON SO, OLD BOY! AT LEAST YOU WON'T HAVE TO WASH IT OUT OF YOUR HAIR WHEN THE MEAL'S OVER!

NEXT MORNING, I WAS LIFTED ON THE BROAD BACK OF MY FAITHFUL VALET, WHO EXPLAINED THAT I WAS ABOUT TO RECEIVE MY MORNING BATH . . .

WHY COULDN'T I HAVE BROKEN A LEG?

PATIENCE, TOBY!

OUR APPEARANCE ON THE VERANDA DREW QUITE A CROWD...

THAT AFTERNOON, WE RECEIVED ANOTHER VISIT FROM MEHEVI . . .

HERE COMES HIS HIGHNESS AGAIN!

WHATEVER THE PURPOSE OF HIS VISIT, HE SEEMS IN A MOST CORDIAL MOOD!

HE BID US FOLLOW HIM OUT OF THE HUT . . .

I WISH I KNEW WHERE THE OLD CODGER IS TAKING US TO!

REALLY, TOBY, YOUR CURIOSITY IS MOST AMAZING!

OUR JOURNEY WAS SOON AT AN END, AND TO MY HORROR, I REALIZED WE WERE IN THE TABOO GROVES OF THE VALLEY* . . .

*A PLACE WHERE RELIGIOUS RITES ARE HELD.

MEHEVI LED US TO A BUILDING CLOSE BY . . .

I'D GIVE MY GOOD RIGHT ARM TO BE BACK ON THE "DOLLY" THIS MINUTE! THIS PLACE GIVES ME THE SHIVERS!

WE FOLLOWED THE CHIEF INTO THE HOUSE . . .

LOOK AT ALL THOSE BLOOMIN' WEAPONS!

THIS, I GATHER, MUST BE THE TRIBE'S ARMORY!

NEXT MORNING, AFTER BEING ABUNDANTLY FEASTED, TOBY AND I ROSE TO DEPART, WHEN MEHEVI MOTIONED US TO REMAIN . . .

ABO! ABO!

DON'T TELL ME THEY'RE GOING TO STUFF US AGAIN!

WAIT! WAIT!

I WONDER WHAT THEY'RE UP TO NOW?

WHATEVER IT IS, IT VITALLY CON-CERNS US, YOU CAN BET ON THAT!

WE SOON PERCEIVED THAT MEHEVI WAS MARSHALLING A GUARD OF HONOR TO ESCORT US BACK TO THE HOUSE OF MARHEYO.

GREAT CAESAR'S GHOST! LOOK AT ALL THAT FOOD WILL YOU?

LOOKS LIKE THE CHIEF IS GOING TO KEEP OLD MARHEYO'S CUPBOARD WELL STOCKED FOR HIS GUESTS OF HONOR!

AS THE PROCESSION MOVED ON . . .

WELL TOBY, WHAT SAY YOU NOW TO YOUR BLOOD-THIRSTY CANNIBALS?

I SAY THEY'RE STILL PLAYING CAT AND MOUSE WITH US! THERE'S NO OTHER WAY OF ACCOUNTING FOR THIS OUTLANDISH DISPLAY OF HOSPITALITY!

AS WE APPROACHED OUR HOUSE, ITS INMATES RUSHED OUT TO RECEIVE US . . .

TOMMO! TOBY!

AS THE DAYS PASSED THE NATIVES CONTINUED. ATTENTION TO US BECAME MORE AND MORE PUZZLING. MY APPREHENSION INCREASED DESPITE THEIR APPARENT KINDNESS, AND I NEVER FOR A MOMENT CEASED PLANNING OUR ESCAPE BEFORE SOMETHING FEARFUL HAPPENED TO US.

ABOUT A WEEK LATER . . .

HOW'S THE OLD LEG COMING ALONG, MATE?

WORSE THAN EVER! I'M AFRAID I'M A GONER, UNLESS I GET SOME MEDICAL ATTENTION SOON!

TO MY HORROR, THERE WAS NO SIGN OF TOBY . . .

TOBY! WHERE'S TOBY?

GETTING NOTHING BUT CONFLICTING REPLIES, I DESPERATELY SOUGHT THE HELP OF THE BEAUTEOUS FAYAWAY AND BESEECHED HER TO TELL ME THE TRUTH . . .

THAT NIGHT, CONFLICTING THOUGHTS RACKED MY WEARY BRAIN . . .

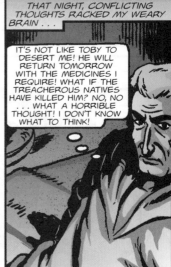

IT'S NOT LIKE TOBY TO DESERT ME! HE WILL RETURN TOMORROW WITH THE MEDICINES I REQUIRE! WHAT IF THE TREACHEROUS NATIVES HAVE KILLED HIM? NO, NO . . . WHAT A HORRIBLE THOUGHT! I DON'T KNOW WHAT TO THINK!

SHE APPEARED GREATLY DISTRESSED AT MY SORROW BUT OFFERED ME NO MORE HOPE THAN THE REST . . .

AWHA! AWHA! TOBY!

ALAS! ALAS! TOBY!

CONVINCED THAT MY COMPANION HAD MET WITH SOME TERRIBLE FATE, I RESIGNED MYSELF TO A LONG STAY AMONG THE UNPREDICTABLE SAVAGES. IN THE DAYS THAT FOLLOWED, SEVERAL AMUSING INCIDENTS OCCURRED WHICH I CANNOT HELP BUT RELATE . . .

THE BUNDLE CONTAINING MY POSSESSIONS HAD BEEN INGENIOUSLY SUSPENDED FROM THE CEILING BY THE NATIVES THE MORNING FOLLOWING OUR ARRIVAL . . .

WISHING TO DO SOME NECESSARY MENDING, I LOWERED THE BUNDLE AND TOOK OUT MY SEWING KIT . . .

AH! TOMMO!

THIS IS A NEW ONE ON THE CURIOUS OLD CODGER!

SUDDENLY, MARHEYO CLAPPED HIS HANDS TO HIS HEAD . . .

AH! AH!

RUSHING TO A CORNER OF THE HOUSE, HE CAME BACK WITH A TORN STRIP OF FADED CALICO AND MOTIONED ME TO MEND IT . . .

HMM! LOOKS LIKE I'M TO BE THE VILLAGE SEAMSTRESS!

THE JOB COMPLETED, MARHEYO GAVE ME A PATERNAL HUG . . .

AND GRASPING HIS SPEAR, SALLIED OUT OF THE HOUSE LIKE A VALIANT KNIGHT, ARRAYED IN A NEW AND COSTLY SUIT OF ARMOR . . .

ONE AFTERNOON, WHILE RECLINING ON MY MAT, MARHEYO RUSHED INTO MY PRESENCE, SHOUTING EXCITEDLY . . .

MAR-NOO PEMI!"

MARNOO IS HERE

IN A FEW MOMENTS, THE NEWCOMER ENTERED THE HOUSE FOLLOWED BY AN EXCITED MOB . . .

AS HE ENTERED, I INVOLUNTARILY ROSE AND OFFERED HIM A SEAT ON THE MAT BESIDE ME . . .

HUH! THE SAVAGE IS EITHER BLIND OR JUST PLAIN CONCEITED!

FOR AN HOUR, THE NATIVES WAITED ON HIM HAND AND FOOT, AND LISTENED, ENTHRALLED, TO HIS TALES OF ADVENTURE . . .

HOW YOU DO? HOW LONG YOU BE IN THIS BAY? YOU LIKE THIS BAY?

SUDDENLY, HE AROSE AND SEATED HIMSELF WITHIN LESS THAN A YARD OF ME . . .

ZOUNDS! WHERE DID YOU LEARN TO SPEAK MY LANGUAGE? WHERE ARE YOU FROM?

ME FROM NUKUHIVA!

NUKUHIVA! AND YOU'RE HERE AMONG THE TYPEES?

AH! ME TABOO! ME GO NUKUHIVA . . . ME GO TYPEE . . . ME GO EVERY-WHERE! NOBODY HARM ME . . . TABOO!

HIS EXPLANATION RECALLED TO MY MIND THE SACRED CUSTOM OF THE TABOO, COMMON AMONG THE ISLANDERS. A PERSON CONSIDERED TABOO IS RESPECTED AND RENDERED SAFE FROM HARM, NO MATTER WHERE HE TRAVELS . . .

BUT TELL ME, MARNOO, WHERE DID YOU LEARN TO SPEAK ENGLISH?

ME CARRIED AWAY TO SEA BY CAPTAIN OF TRADING VESSEL . . . SPEND THREE YEARS IN SIDNEY, AUSTRALIA! LEARN TO SPEAK LIKE WHITE MAN!

I TOLD HIM OF MY ARRIVAL ON THE ISLANDS AND QUESTIONED HIM ABOUT TOBY . . .

TOBY? NO, NO! ME KNOW NOTHING! ME NO SEE WHITE MAN LONG TIME!

ACTING ON THE IMPULSE, I APPEALED TO HIM TO HELP ME TO ESCAPE TO NUKUHIVA . . .

NO, NO! YOU MUST STAY HERE IN TYPE GOOD HERE! PLENT FOOD . . . PLENTY EVERYTHING! NATIVE NO LIKE YOU GO T NUKUHIVA!

MY LEG, WHICH HAD BEEN ON THE MEND, SOON TURNED FOR THE WORSE AGAIN AND I DESPAIRED OF EVER GETTING OUT OF THE VALLEY. AN OCCURRENCE SOME TIME LATER AFFECTED ME MOST POWERFULLY...

BESIDE MY BUNDLE OF BELONGINGS, THERE WERE SUSPENDED IN THE HUT A NUMBER OF PACKAGES WHICH HAD OFTEN EXCITED MY CURIOSITY...

THE ALARM OF THE SAVAGES FILLED ME WITH A FOREBODING OF EVIL...

NOW WHAT CAN THEY BE UP TO WITH THOSE BUNDLES THAT MAKES THEM SO JITTERY?

ONE DAY, MY UNEXPECTED ARRIVAL IN THE HOUSE SEEMED TO THROW ITS INMATES INTO GREAT CONFUSION...

I WONDER WHAT MAKES THEM SO... UH HUH, IT MUST BE SOMETHING THEY'VE GOT IN THOSE PACKAGES!

DETERMINED TO SEE FOR MYSELF, I PUSHED ON, DISREGARDING THE RESTRAINING HANDS OF MY HOST...

A MOMENT LATER, A HORRIBLE SIGHT MET MY EYES...

GOOD HEAVENS! SHRUNKEN HEADS!

...WO OF THE THREE
ERE HEADS OF THE
SLANDERS; BUT THE
HIRD, TO MY HORROR,
WAS THE HEAD OF A
WHITE MAN...

A WHITE MAN! *TOBY!*
NO, NO, IT COULDN'T
BE! I'M LETTING MY
IMAGINATION RUN AWAY
WITH ME!

BEFORE I COULD RECOVER FROM
THE TERROR WHICH HAD GRIPPED ME,
THE FATAL PACKAGES WERE AGAIN
...STED ALOFT.

THE NATIVES NOW GATHERED AROUND ME AND
TRIED TO CONVINCE ME THAT WHAT I HAD SEEN
WERE THE HEADS OF THREE HAPPAR WARRIORS,
SLAIN IN BATTLE...

I WAS NOW MORE DETERMINED
THAN EVER TO MAKE MY ESCAPE
FROM THESE SAVAGE HEATHENS.
THREE WEEKS AFTER THESE
EVENTS, I WAS ASTOUNDED BY
THE SUDDEN APPEARANCE IN THE
HUT OF THE ONE-EYED CHIEF,
MOW-MOW...

TOBY PEMI-
ENA'

WHAT?
TOBY?

'TOBY HAS ARRIVED HERE.

I LEAPED WILDLY TO MY FEET, INSENSIBLE TO THE PAIN IN MY LIMB AND CALLED OUT TO MY VALET...

KORY-KORY, TOBY! TOBY PEMI!

THE NEXT MOMENT, I WAS ON KORY-KORY'S BACK MAKING MY WAY TO THE TI, CHIEF MEHEVI'S RESIDENCE, FOLLOWED BY THE SHOUTING NATIVES...

AT THE TI, I TRIED TO MAKE THE CHIEF UNDER-STAND I WAS GOING DOWN TO THE SEA...

MEHEVI, TOBY PEMI! PEMI ENA!

TO THIS THE CHIEF OBJECTED AND MOTIONED KORY-KORY TO BRING ME INTO THE HOUSE...

MY PROTESTS WERE IN VAIN, AND IN A FEW MOMENTS, I FOUND MYSELF IN THE TI, SURROUNDED BY A NOISY GROUP...

HAD A WEIRD FEELING THAT MY OWN FATE WAS ABOUT TO BE DECIDED. I RENEWED MY PLEAS TO MEHEVI, WHO FINALLY YIELDED AND RELUCTANTLY GRANTED MY REQUEST...

URGING KORY-KORY TO HURRY, WE LEFT THE TI, FOLLOWED BY ABOUT FIFTY NATIVES...

IT'S NOW OR NEVER!

AS WE PROCEEDED, THE NATIVES TOOK TURNS IN CARRYING ME...

COME ON, YOU HEATHEN! THIS TIME I'M GETTING AWAY IF I HAVE TO DIE IN THE ATTEMPT!

SUDDENLY, WE WERE MET BY A PARTY OF SOME TWENTY ISLANDERS...

AS THE TWO GROUPS STOPPED TO CONFER, I BESEECHED THE MAN WHO CARRIED ME TO PROCEED WITHOUT HIS COMPANIONS...

COME ON, YOU DEVIL! DON'T WAIT FOR THOSE CONFOUNDED NIT-WITS!

AS I PLEADED WITH THE SAVAGE, KORY-KORY CAME RUNNING TO MY SIDE...

TOMMO! TOMMO!

WHAT IS IT, KORY-KORY?

TOBY OWLEE PEMI!'

HOW I SUSTAINED THE SHOCK CAUSED BY THIS NEWS, I SHALL NEVER KNOW. THE NATIVES HAVING LEARNED THE TRUTH ABOUT TOBY, I WAS OBSESSED WITH THE FEAR THAT I WOULD NOW BE TAKEN BACK...

'TOBY HAS NOT ARRIVED.'

MY FEARS WERE SOON REALIZED...

MIGHT HAVE KNOWN IT WAS A FALSE ALARM! BUT THERE MUST BE SOME BOATS DOWN THERE EVEN IF TOBY IS NOT WITH THEM!

AS I RENEWED MY PLEA, THE NATIVES ALLOWED ME TO GO OUTSIDE THE HOUSE, BUT THEY ANGRILY REFUSED TO CARRY ME ANY FURTHER...

SEIZING A SPEAR IN DESPERATION, I RESUMED THE PATH TO THE SEA...

I'VE GOT TO MAKE THOSE BOATS BEFORE THEY LEAVE!

GLANCING BACK, I PERCEIVED THE NATIVES WERE ENGAGED IN SOME CONTROVERSY, AS THOUGH SOME DIFFERENCE OF OPINION HAD ARISEN ABOUT ME...

GOOD! WHILE THEY ARGUE, I'LL KEEP GOING IF I HAVE TO MAKE IT ON ONE LEG!

I WAS SOON AGAIN SURROUNDED BY THE SAVAGES WHO SEEMED ABOUT TO COME TO BLOWS...

MARHEYO!

PLACING HIS ARM ON MY SHOULDER, MARHEYO PRONOUNCED THE ONE EXPRESSIVE ENGLISH WORD I HAD TAUGHT HIM...

HOME, TOMMO!

GOOD OLD MARHEYO! I'LL NEVER FORGET YOU FOR THIS!

FOLLOWED BY MARHEYO, KORY-KORY AND FAYAWAY, I SOON HEARD THE ROAR OF THE SURF BREAKING UPON THE BEACH...

AS WE DREW NEAR THE BEACH, I PERCEIVED AN ENGLISH WHALEBOAT CLOSE INTO THE SHORE...

THE OPEN SEA AT LAST!

I RECOGNIZED A NATIVE FROM OAHU' WHO HAD OFTEN BEEN ABOARD THE "DOLLY" WHILE SHE LAY IN NUKUHIVA...

IT'S KARAKOEE! AHOY, KARAKOEE! I'M COMING!

'HAWAIIAN ISLAND

I REMEMBERED KARAKOEE HAD TOLD ME HIS PERSON WAS TABOO IN ALL THE VALLEYS OF THE ISLAND AND THE SIGHT OF HIM FILLED MY HEART WITH DELIGHT...

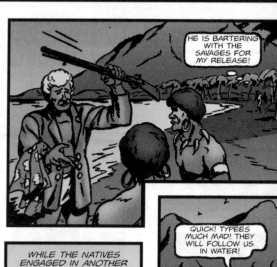

HE IS BARTERING WITH THE SAVAGES FOR MY RELEASE!

MY JOY WAS SHORT-LIVED AS SAW THE SAVAGES ANGRILY WAVE HIM BACK TO THE BOAT...

WHILE THE NATIVES ENGAGED IN ANOTHER CONFLICT CONCERNING ME, I GATHERED MY LAST STRENGTH AND RUSHED TOWARDS THE BOAT...

QUICK! TYPEES MUCH MAD! THEY WILL FOLLOW US IN WATER!

THE OTHER SAVAGES WERE TAKEN CARE OF BY OUR ROWERS...

THERE GOES MY LAST BARRIER TO FREEDOM!

SOON, A LARGE WHALER LOOMED UP IN THE BAY...

WHAT SHIP IS THAT, KARAKOEE?

THE "JULIA!" I TELL THEM WHITE MAN CAPTURED BY TYPEES AND THEY SEND ME IN BOAT T GET YOU.

ONE MORE THING, KARAKOEE. HOW DID YOU KNOW I WAS BEING HELD BY THE TYPEES?

MARNOO. HE TABOO LIKE ME. HE TELL ME; I TELL CAPTAIN OF JULIA; YOU KNOW REST!

YOU DID A GOOD JOB, MY FRIEND! YOU SAVED MY LIFE, AND I SHALL NEVER FORGET YOU FOR IT!

I JOINED UP WITH THE CREW OF THE "JULIA," AND SPENT TWO EVENTFUL YEARS ROAMING THE SOUTH SEAS BEFORE I RETURNED HOME. IT WAS SOME TIME LATER THAT I RECEIVED THE SHOCK OF MY LIFE BY RUNNING INTO TOBY, WHOM I HAD GIVEN UP FOR LOST...

TOBY, OLD BOY! I CAN HARDLY BELIEVE IT'S YOU!

IT'S ME ALL RIGHT, MATEY. I HARDLY EXPECTED TO SEE YOU AGAIN!

I PRESSED HIM TO TELL ME THE STORY OF HIS MYSTERIOUS DISAPPEARANCE...

THE MORNING I LEFT YOU, I WAS ACCOMPANIED BY A LARGE PARTY OF NATIVES, BEARING FRUIT AND BREAD FOR TRADING WITH THE BOATS THAT HAD BEEN SIGHTED IN THE BAY!

SUDDENLY, A STRANGE SOUND CAME THROUGH THE GROVE BEYOND...

WHAT WAS THAT?

MOW-MOW.

"UP AHEAD, MOW-MOW, WHO HAD PRECEDED US, WAS STRIKING HIS LANCE AGAINST THE HOLLOW BOUGH OF A TREE..."

HAPPAR! HAPPAR!

IT LOOKS LIKE WE'RE IN FOR SOME TROUBLE!

"AS THE DIN INCREASED, I ASKED ONE OF THE YOUNG NATIVES FOR THE LOAN OF HIS SPEAR..."

TYPEE
HERMAN MELVILLE

On July 11, 1842, the ship
Potomac of Nantucket, lying in the
harbor of Taiohae at Nuku Hiva in
the Marquesas Islands, recorded in
its log: "Ship *Acushnet* of
— intending to lay off for
a day or two & send boat
for her men who have
deserted." Of the
Acushnet's five runaways,
three were caught two days
later.

One of the two men who evaded
capture was the young Herman
Melville.

Herman Melville was
born on August 1, 1819, into
a well-established, but no
longer very well-off, New
York family. He went to sea
for the first time while still
in his teens, sailing as a
cabin boy on a ship bound
for Liverpool. In 1841, as a
young man of twenty-one,
Melville sailed for the
South Seas on the
whaler *Acushnet*.
Eighteen months into the
voyage, he and a com-
panion deserted the ship
in the Marquesas Islands
and lived there for a
month among the natives.
Melville left the island

aboard an Australian trader, and
made his way first to Tahiti and
then to Honolulu. There, in 1843,
he enlisted as a seaman aboard the
U.S. Navy frigate *United
States*. On his return to
America and his discharge,
Melville turned his hand to
writing.

Melville's first novel,
*Typee: A Peep at
Polynesian Life*, appeared in 1846.
The book was loosely based upon
his experiences after jumping ship
in the Marquesas, and quickly
proved popular. The first edition,
published in England, was soon
followed by a second, American
edition. Although the American
edition contained some new material—an epilogue telling about the
escape of the narrator's friend
Toby—the text was also cut in
places by the author. Some of the
more explicit passages about the
easygoing sexuality of the
Marquesan Islanders
(explicit at least by the
standards of Victorian-era
America), and the harshest
of Melville's criticisms of
missionary activities in the
South Seas, are missing
from the later text.
(Modern editions usually
follow the first English

version, with the addition of the American edition's epilogue.)

More novels followed over the course of the author's life—*Omoo, Mardi, Redburn, White-Jacket, Moby-Dick*, and *Billy Budd*, among others—but *Typee* was the book that first brought Herman Melville fame and launched his career.

Herman Melville's actual time among the Marquesan islanders was brief—only about four weeks, instead of the four months that his alter ego "Tommo" spends in the book—and his experiences there could not by themselves support the length of an entire book. As a result, *Typee* contains two other main elements worked in among the tale of Tommo's adventures. One is a travelogue, the "peep at Polynesian life" promised to the reader in the book's subtitle. The history and geography of the Marquesas Islands, their climate, landscape, and vegetation, the lives and customs of their inhabitants, are all described at length. The other element is political and philosophical, and deals with the destruction of the native Polynesian culture through contact with Western civilization—represented in the South Seas primarily by sailors and missionaries.

How much of *Typee* is autobiog-

Tattoos: Sailors and Islanders

The Polynesian islanders had plenty of leisure time in which to practice their decorative arts—wood carving, the manufacture of bark cloth (<u>tapa</u>) and, most notably, tattooing. Complex designs were worked into the skin of the person being tattooed, using instruments of wood and bone. The more elaborate the tattooing, the greater the social status of the person bearing it. In *Typee*, Melville discusses the use of tattooing among the islanders, and makes its meaning and importance clear to the reader. His semi-fictional alter ego, Tommo, however, resists acquiring the native tattoos:

"When the king first expressed his wish to me [that I should be tattooed], I made known to him my utter abhorrence of the measure, and worked myself into such a state of excitement, that he absolutely stared at me in amazement. It e[vi]dently surpassed his majesty's comprehen[sion] how any sober-minded and sensible individual could entertain the least possib[le] objection to so beautifying an operation.

"Soon afterwards he repeated his sugge[s]tion, and meeting with a like repulse, showed some symptoms of displeasure at m[y] obduracy. On his third time renewing his request, I plai[n]ly perceived that something must be done, or my visage was ruined for ever; I there[-]fore screwed up my courag[e] to the sticking point, and declared my willingness to have both arms tattooed fr[om] just above the wrist to the shoulder. His majesty was greatly pleased at the propo[si]tion, and I was congratulati[ng] myself with having thus compromised the matter, when he intimated that as a thing [of]

IN A FEW MOMENTS, THE NEWCOMER ENTERED THE HOUSE FOLLOWED BY AN EXCITED MOB.

raphy, and how much is exaggeration for dramatic effect, or even outright fiction, is hard to determine. Melville himself, in his Prologue to the book, describes the work in terms that have as much to do with sailors' yarns as they do with sober recorded fact:

"More than three years have elapsed since the occurrence of the events recorded in this volume. The interval, with the exception of the last few months, has been chiefly spent by the author tossing about on the wide ocean. Sailors are the only class of men who now-a-days see anything like stirring adventure; and many things which to fire-side people appear strange and romantic, to them seem as commonplace as a jacket out at elbows. Yet, notwithstanding the familiarity of sailors with all sorts of curious adventure, the incidents recorded in the following pages have often served, when 'spun as a yarn,' not only to relieve the weariness of many a night-watch at sea, but to excite the warmest sympathies of the author's shipmates. He has been, therefore, led to think that his story could scarcely fail to interest those who are less familiar than the sailor with a life of adventure."

course my face was first to undergo the operation.

"... A fact which I soon afterwards learned augmented my apprehension. The whole system of tattooing was, I found, connected with their religion; and it was evident, therefore, that they were resolved to make a convert of me."

At the same time, Melville makes it clear to his readers that the sailors themselves bear tattoos, in a passage describing the reception of King Moana of Nuku Hiva and his wife aboard a naval vessel:

"The ship's company crowding into the gangway to view the sight, soon arrested her majesty's attention. She singled out from their number an old <u>salt</u>, whose bare arms and feet, and exposed breast were covered with as many inscriptions in India ink as the lid of an Egyptian sarcophagus. Notwithstanding all the sly hints and remonstrances of the French officers, she immediately approached the man, and pulling further open the bosom of his duck frock, and rolling up the leg of his wide trowsers, she gazed with admiration at the bright blue and vermilion pricking, thus disclosed to view."

So it's not necessarily the concept of tattooing itself that is repugnant to Tommo. Possibly his reluctance springs from the idea that acquiring the native tattoos—as opposed to sailor's tattoos—would mark a shift of allegiance from one society to the other that he is unwilling to make? As he says himself, "they were resolved to make a convert of me." Possibly, also, Tommo's unwillingness to commit to such a shift of allegiance is what causes the attitude of the islanders to change toward him.

In fact we do not know, because the narrator himself does not know, what the islanders themselves thought that they were offering Tommo when they urged him to be tattooed. Nor can we be sure what their ultimate plans for Tommo's fate might have been: indefinite captivity, continued attempts to "convert" him into part of the tribe, or main course at a cannibal feast. But there's a good chance that what the narrator thinks is going on, and what the islanders think is going on, are two different stories—one of which (since we have only Tommo's point of view to go on) we can never know.

Tommo: the narrator, a young American sailor, based upon Herman Melville himself. "Tommo" is the Typeean pronunciation of "Tom", the name the narrator gives himself because he thinks that his hosts/captors may find his real name difficult to pronounce. Melville probably took his alias from the name of his cousin Thomas Melville, who had been aboard the USS *Vincennes* when that ship visited Nuku Hiva in 1829.

Toby: another sailor off the *Dolly*, who jumps ship with Tommo and becomes his partner in adventure. Toby's real-world counterpart was the sailor Richard Tobias Greene, who did in fact show up again after the publication of the English edition of *Typee* (which had ended with Tommo still wondering about his companion's ultimate fate). The two men kept in touch thereafter, and "Toby" eventually named his son Herman Melville Greene after his friend.

Kory-Kory: a young Typeean man who cares for Tommo while he's ill in the house of Marheyo and Tinor.

Fayaway: the Typeean girl who becomes Tommo's particular friend.

Mehevi: the "king", or paramount chief, of Taipivai, the valley of the Typees. With his people's traditional enemies the Happars making raids into Taipivai from the next valley over, and with French warships at anchor in the harbor beyond *that*, the last thing that Mehevi needed in 1842 was a couple of deserters from an American whaler showing up to complicate things. Urging Tommo to accept tribal tattoes, and encouraging the sailor's relationship with Fayaway, may have been attempts on Mehevi's part to deal with the problem of the newcomers by bringing them into the Typeean community.

Marheyo: one of the Typees, in whose house Tommo lives during his stay.

Tinor: Marheyo's wife.

Marnoo: An islander who is allowed by custom to travel freely from one valley to another, even though the tribes that live there may be at war. He speaks some English, and has sympathy for Tommo in his difficulties.

Mow-Mow: a Typeean chief, subordinate to Mehevi. He is at times hostile to Toby and Tommo, and something of an adversary.

Cannibalism: a Matter of Fact and Fiction

The cannibalism motif is even stronger in *Typee* proper than in the Classics Illustrated adaptation. In the book, the horrifying discovery that causes the narrator to resolve upon escape is not merely a bundle of shrunken heads. He finds the heads earlier, and is shaken by the discovery (less of the heads themselves than of the fact that one of them had belonged to a white man rather than an islander). The real shocker, however, comes after the men of the valley have been absent for some days at a mysterious feast:

" ...I observed a curiously carved vessel of wood, of considerable size, with a cover placed over it, of the same material, and which resembled in shape a small canoe. It was surrounded by a low railing of bamboos, the top of which was scarcely a foot from the ground. As the vessel had been placed in its present position since my last visit, I at once concluded that it must have some connection with the recent festival; and, prompted by a curiosity I could not repress, in passing it I raised one end of the cover; at the same moment the chiefs, perceiving my design, loudly ejaculated, 'Taboo! taboo!' But the slight glimpse sufficed; my eyes fell upon the disordered members of a human skeleton, the bones still fresh with moisture, and with particles of flesh clinging to them here and there!"

Western civilization in general has an ongoing fascination with the idea of cannibalism. It's perhaps our society's most serious taboo—the eating of human flesh is much more effectively forbidden to us than, say, murder or incest. For this reason, one of our most effective ways to label somebody or some culture as "other" is to accuse them of cannibalism. This "use" of cannibalism as a concept eventually led some scholars (notably W. Arens in 1979's *The Man Eating Myth*) to assert that actual cannibalism never existed. Rather, these scholars claimed, the idea of cannibalism was essentially propaganda, developed in order to "otherize" native and/or primitive peoples.

Melville himself hints at this process when he describes how the

Typees, themselves characterized by the other islanders as the most vicious and incorrigible of cannibals, say the same thing about the supposedly friendly Happar:

"Our Typee friends availed themselves of the recent disaster…to exhort us to a due appreciation of the blessings we enjoyed among them; contrasting their own generous reception of us with the animosity of their neighbors. They likewise dwelt upon the cannibal propensities of the Happars, a subject which they were perfectly aware could not fail to alarm us; while at the same time they earnestly disclaimed all participation in so horrid a custom….

"Happar keekeeno nuee," [Kory-Kory] exclaimed; "nuee, nuee, ki ki kannaka!—ah! owle mortar-kee!" which signifies, "Terrible fellows those Happars!—devour an amazing quantity of men!—ah, shocking bad!"

The assertion that cannibalism—as an institution rather than as a fictional concept—simply did not exist prompted a response in the form of further and deeper research into the issue by anthropologists, archaeologists, and historians. General opinion now favors the reality of cannibalism in historical cultures, from the Aztecs of Mexico to the islanders of the South Pacific.

Anthropologists divide cannibal societies into two groups. Endo-cannibals eat the flesh of members of their own tribe or family, usually as part of the funeral ritual. (The ritual of the Catholic Mass, in which bread and wine become the body and blood of Christ, is a symbolic form of endo-cannibalism.) Exo-cannibals, on the other hand, eat the flesh of other tribes or families, usually their enemies, frequently in the aftermath of war. The Taipi (Typee) of Nuku Hiva, like many other Polynesians, practiced exo-cannibalism.

The sailors who came to Nuku Hiva had their own legends and histories of cannibalism, in spite of the intensity of the Western taboo against it. The crew of the whaling ship *Essex*, which was struck and sunk by a wounded sperm whale in 1820, spent over two months adrift in the Pacific in open whaleboats, and were ultimately forced to draw lots in order to determine who among them should be killed and eaten to keep the others alive. Even more famous, in some ways, was the wreck of the French ship *Medusa* in 1816, which resulted in 150 people being set adrift in the eastern Atlantic on a hastily built raft measuring only 67 x 24 feet. The raft of the *Medusa* saw mutiny and murder, as well as cannibalism; out of the 150 on the raft, only 15 were still alive when rescue came. In these cases, the descent into cannibalism represented more than the desperation born of extreme hunger; it also represented the collapse of the social structures which made bearable the unnatural crowding and forced intimacy of life at sea.

The *Essex* and the *Medusa* were well-known ships. Melville himself had met the son of one of the *Essex* survivors during his time at sea, and he knew the story. In 1819, the *Medusa* incident became the subject of a famous and controversial painting by Théodore Géricault, *Scene of a Shipwreck* (better known as *The Raft of the Medusa*) thus making the conduct of her survivors notorious even beyond the world of seafarers. But both of these disasters were only known because there *were* survivors. Other, less fortunate ships vanished completely, their fate only guessed at when the vessel in question failed to return to port; and who could tell what those lost crews might have been forced to endure before they died?

For Melville and his fellow sailors, such a fate represented an ever-present danger. It's not surprising that the crews of American whaling vessels would simultaneously fear and be fascinated by the Pacific islanders, who enjoyed a seemingly Edenic existence …and who regularly practiced cannibalism just the same.

Jumping Ship

Herman Melville was far from being the only sailor in the American whale fishery to jump ship in the South Pacific. The problem was a common one, and it sprang directly from the conditions of life aboard ship on the long whaling voyages. Out of the *Acushnet's* original crew of twenty-six, thirteen (including Melville and his companion, not to mention the first and third mates) jumped ship at one point or another.

One reason for this high rate of desertion was the extreme length of the South Seas whaling voyages. Captains were reluctant to turn back before either their supplies ran out or their ships' holds were full of whale oil, expeditions of two or three years were not

SIX MONTHS AT SEA! SIX MONTHS OUT OF SIGHT OF LAND, CRUISING AFTER THE SPERM WHALE BENEATH THE SCORCHING SUN OF THE EQUATOR .. THE SKY ABOVE, THE SEA AROUND, AND NOTHING ELSE..

WITH HOPE STILL BEATING IN MY HEART, I ADDRESS MYSELF TO THE POOR, OLD SHIP…

COURAGE, OLD LASS! I HOPE TO SEE YOU SOON WITHIN A BISCUIT'S TOSS OF THE MERRY LAND, RIDING SNUGLY AT ANCHOR IN SOME GREEN CAVE!

uncommon. The *Acushnet* had spent eighteen months at sea, with only two port calls, when Melville made up his mind to leave her; the voyage ultimately lasted five years.

Added to the length of the voyages was the nature of whale hunting. Life aboard a whaler meant weeks, even months of boredom. The ships spent most of their time cruising slowly about those parts of the ocean where the great whales congregated, in the hopes of seeing a whale show up somewhere within view of the ship's lookout. Given the size of the Pacific ocean, this required as much sheer good luck as it did anything else. Sighting and killing a whale broke up the monotony with a few hours of extreme danger followed by brutal, messy physical labor—and then it was back to monotony again.

Sailors often had to endure life under capricious, brutal, or downright crazy captains and officers: men like Captain Samuel Winegar of the whale ship *Julian*, who in 1859 refused to cut loose the carcass of a large whale the ship had just taken, in spite of an Arctic storm that threatened to drive the *Julian* onto the rocks. "I had rather go to the Devil with a whale," he explained later in his diary, "than go in to New Bedford without one." Another captain, George Pomeroy, was a spiritualist, who regularly sought advice from his "Spirit Friends and Guardian Angles" [sic]; Pomeroy's eccentricity was tolerated by the vessel's owners because his ships regularly returned to New Bedford with full holds. Other captains were drunk

The Breadfruit Tree

The narrator of *Typee* has a lot to say about the abundance of fruit on the island, and the easy availability of food. At the beginning of the story, the two deserters are willing to chance striking out into the interior of the island because they assume that there will be tropical fruits available for them to eat. (As it happens, their journey takes them across the rocky mountain ridges, and not through the fertile lowlands, and they nearly starve before reaching Taipivai.) Of all the fruits of the South Seas, the one which makes perhaps the greatest impression on Tommo, as it did on most Europeans, is the evocatively-named breadfruit:

WE HAVE OUR CHOICE BETWEEN STARVING TO DEATH OR MAKING OUR DESCENT AND HOPING FOR THE BEST!

AFTER FIVE DAYS OF GREAT TOIL AND UNTOLD DANGERS, WE ARRIVED IN THE VALLEY AND PUSHED STEADILY ONWARD...

LOOK, TOBY! ISN'T THAT A FRUIT TREE?

GREAT SCOTT! MANNA FROM HEAVEN!

"The bread-fruit tree, in its glorious prime, is a grand and towering object, forming the same feature in a Marquesan landscape that the patriarchal elm does in New England scenery. The latter tree it not a little resembles in height, in the wide spread of its stalwart branches, and in its venerable and imposing aspect.... At a certain season of the year, when the fruit of the hundred groves of the valley has reached its maturity, and hangs in golden spheres from every branch, the islanders assemble in harvest groups, and garner in the abundance which surrounds them."

But what, actually, is the breadfruit tree?

or otherwise incapable, like Richard Veeder of the whaler *William Gifford*, who in 1871 became so habitually violent and intoxicated during a Marquesan cruise that his crew seized him, tied him up, and sailed for Tahiti, there to put their case before the American consul—who was sufficiently convinced of their justification that he removed Veeder from command and sent the *William Gifford* on to San Francisco with another captain in charge.

The captain in *Typee*, while harsh and authoritarian, is nowhere in this league. (Melville dealt with the problem of unfit authority figures in other books, most notably in *Moby Dick*.) What the book's narrator seems to worry about most is:

Bad food. Tommo is preoccupied with food, both on ship and ashore. This isn't surprising: the food aboard ship was awful.

"Delicate morsels of beef and pork [says the narrator], cut on scientific principles from every part of the animal, and of all conceivable shapes and sizes, are carefully packed in salt, and stored away in

---

"Breadfruit" is the English name of the *oro* or *uru*, (scientific name, *Artocarpus altilis*) a tropical tree that grows on the islands of the South Pacific Ocean—particularly, as it happens, in the Marquesas. The tree bears a fruit about the size of a small melon, with a rough rind and a white, mealy pulp. The pulp, when baked, is somewhat sweet, with a soft texture—it has, as Melville's narrator tells us, "a mild and pleasing flavor." Breadfruit pulp can also be dried and ground to make biscuits, bread, and puddings. In addition, the inner bark of the breadfruit tree can be made into cloth, and the wood into furniture and canoes.

> OH, OH! LOOKS LIKE I STILL HAVE TO LEARN THE TECHNIQUE OF EATING POEE-POEE!

> YOU'VE SURE MADE A MESS OF THINGS, OLD MAN!

Even the tree's milky sap can be used in a waterproofing compound.

For people accustomed, like the Europeans and Americans, to staple foods that were the product of laborious agriculture, the breadfruit tree was a wonder, something very close to the biblical Tree of Life. The fact that this marvelous tree grew in the earthly paradise of the South Seas reinforced that impression. The tree's English name reflects the heavy emotional and philosophical baggage it was forced to carry: "bread," as in "give us this day our daily bread", is a kind of symbolic shorthand for all that which sustains life.

barrels; affording a never-ending variety in their different degrees of toughness, and in the peculiarities of their saline properties. Choice old water too, decanted into stout six-barrel casks, and two pints of which is allowed every day to each soul on board; together with ample store of sea-bread, previously reduced to a state of petrifaction, with a view to preserve it either from decay or consumption in the ordinary mode, are likewise provided for the nourishment and gastronomic enjoyment of the crew."

Other whaling-ship narratives of the period report foul water, "sour & wormy" bread, and molasses "2-3 inches deep in cockroaches."

In spite of the food's poor quality, there was the perennial question of whether or not crew members were getting their due share. In the previous century, part of the quarrel of *H.M.S. Bounty*'s crew with their captain lay in their concern over the rations, and their fear that Captain Bligh, in his desire to save money on the voyage, was failing to give them the share to which they were entitled by naval regulations. Later, after the famous mutiny, the men who were cast adrift with Bligh in the ship's launch endured an even more stringent rationing of the available food: a "damned economy," as one of the others put it, of one-twelfth of a pound of bread and a quarter pint of water a day. (While Bligh and the men in the *Bounty's* launch did not, in fact, resort to cannibal-

ism during their long journey from Tahiti to the Dutch East Indies, the possibility of it could not have been far from their minds. Bligh himself at one point wrote in his log: "My allowance satisfies me, knowing I can have no more. This perhaps does not admit me to be a proper judge on a story of miserable people like us at last driven to the necessity of destroying one another for food…")

Given the necessity of dividing up and measuring out rations while at sea; and the ever-present background fear of shipwreck and starvation—and looming behind *that*, the specter of cannibalism— it's not surprising that the natural bounty of the islands was enough by itself to prompt sailors to desert.

The Noble Savage and the Pastoral Ideal

To the explorers and traders of the 18th and early 19th centuries, the islands of the South Seas seemed to be the embodiment of two of western civilization's favorite archetypes. One was the myth of a time in the world's past when people lived together in harmony, when war and hunger and greed were unknown and the earth itself supplied all of humanity's simple wants. Greek and Roman mythology called that time the Golden Age; the Bible told of the Garden of Eden; and writers and artists from the Middle Ages through the Renaissance and beyond invented their own countries—Arcadia, Cocaigne, the Forest of Arden—where life was peaceful and simple, and conflict remained unknown.

Artists' descriptions of this ideal world varied, of course, but tended to have certain predictable things in common. Whether the accounts spoke of the Garden of Eden or of the Forest of Arden, the ideal place was in the country, not the city. The inhabitants never supported themselves by business or by serious farming; they lived by idealized versions of hunting and herding. (The reality level in these visions of the simple life was usually somewhere on the level of Queen Marie Antoinette of France pretending to be a dairy-maid at Le Petit Trianon: real hunters and shepherds need not apply.) The land in these wonderful places gave food without the need for backbreaking toil; the weather was always mild, with neither the killing cold of winter nor the summer's sweltering heat. In some versions of the ideal society, as in Eden before the Fall, clothing was optional—and so, too, Melville found the natives of Polynesia. "She wore the habitual summer garb of Eden," he says of one of the Island girls, a direct reference to her innocence and her state of unity with nature, as well as to her state of undress.

Money in all its forms was conspicuously absent in the golden world. The land itself supplied the inhabitants with all their needs, and they (not being greedy, unlike—by implication—the artist's contemporary audience) had no need to trade for anything more than the land could provide. Also missing from Arden/Eden was, often, the private ownership of land, as well as any other aspect of modern society that the artist blamed for its current ills. The pastoral image was one of innocence, contrasted with the corruption that was modern reality. The main thing about the Golden Age was that it was always either long ago or far away, or both—never here and now.

War and interpersonal conflict were usually included in the list of modern ills missing from depictions of this vanished and distant ideal. What, then, was an artist to do when the native peoples who *should* be behaving like inhabitants of the Golden Age turned out to be violent and warlike, and as prone to conflict as their corrupt "civilized" brethren? Simple: invoke a second, equally handy archetype—the Noble Savage, as popularized in the 18th century by the French philosopher Jean-Jacques Rousseau and a host of lesser writers, and in the 19th century by America's own James Fenimore Cooper. Noble Savages were not absolutely required to be peaceful, provided that they were courageous and freedom-loving and magnanimous. (Cooper's Indians, in *The Last of the Mohicans* and other works, were almost all Noble Savages; so, after a fashion, was his huntsman-hero, Hawkeye.) By Herman Melville's day, with the American tribes being forced out of their ancestral lands to make room for the expanding white population, the Noble Savage also had to be relocated. The South Sea Islands made an ideal spot.

Nuku Hiva, 1842: Trouble in Paradise

When young Herman Melville and Richard Tobias Greene decided to take their informal leave of the *Acushnet* on Nuku Hiva, they plunged unawares into a place and a culture already at a point of crisis.

Nuku Hiva is the second largest of the Marquesas Islands, a group of ten volcanic islands in the southern Pacific Ocean. The native Marquesan Islanders are Polynesians, a people who—like the Europeans after them—were relatively recent arrivals in the area. The current view is that their ancestors were driven out of the Malay Archipelago by invaders in about the 2nd century B.C. The Polynesians were superb sailors and long distance navigators, and by the 13th and 14th centuries A.D. they had spread out over most of the Pacific.

Nuku Hiva is a typical volcanic island of the type described by Herman Melville at the beginning of *Typee*. The landscape is marked by "bold rock-bound coasts, with the surf beating high against the lofty cliffs ...broken here and there into deep inlets,

which open to the view thickly wooded valleys, separated by the spurs of mountains clothed with tufted grass, and sweeping down towards the sea from an elevated and furrowed interior ...."

These valleys, separated by high ridges, formed the territories of the various tribes of Nuku Hiva, among them the Teii, the Happa'a (Melville's Happar), and the Taipi (Typee).

The first Europeans came to the Marquesas in July of 1595, when Spanish explorers under the command of Alvaro de Mendaña visited the southern islands. The encounter was not a peaceful one—the Spanish killed a number of the islanders. Mendaña named the group of islands "Las Marquesas de Mendoza" after his patron, García Hurtado de Mendoza, Marquis of Cañate, then serving as the Viceroy of Peru.

Further contacts with Europeans had to wait for some time. The Western exploration of the South Seas was a slow process, made difficult by the vast expanse of the Pacific and the widely scattered nature of the islands. Nevertheless, by the early 19th century, western ships, sailing in the cause of politics and commerce, began once more to visit the Marquesas. The islands were rich in sandalwood, and in the breadfruit trees that promised food without labor. They were also a popular place for whaling ships like the *Dolly* (or Melville's own *Acushnet*) to break their long voyages and put in for rest and resupply.

Missionaries in Eden

Commerce, in the form of the whaling ships, was followed in short order by religion, in the form of missionaries. Melville's comments on the missionaries were not usually favorable. To quote one characteristic passage from *Typee*:

"Among the islands of Polynesia, no sooner are the images overturned, the temples demolished, and the idolaters converted into *nominal* Christians, than disease, vice, and premature death make their appearance. The depopulated land is then recruited from the rapacious hordes of enlightened individuals who settle themselves within its borders, and clamorously announce the progress of the Truth. Neat villas, trim gardens, shaven lawns, spires, and cupolas arise, while the poor savage soon finds himself an interloper in the country of his fathers, and that too on the very site of the hut where he was born. The spontaneous fruits of the earth, which God in his wisdom had ordained for the support of the indolent natives, remorselessly seized upon and appropriated by the stranger, are devoured before the eyes of the starving inhabitants, or sent on board the numerous vessels which now touch at their shores.

"When the famished wretches are cut off in this manner from their natural supplies, they are told by their benefactors to work and earn their support by the sweat of their brows! But to no fine gentleman born to hereditary opulence does manual labor come more unkindly than to the luxurious Indian when thus robbed of the bounty of Heaven. Habituated to a life of indolence, he cannot and will not exert himself; and want, disease, and vice, all evils of foreign growth, soon terminate his miserable existence.

"But what matters all this? Behold the glorious result!—The abominations of Paganism have given way to the pure rites of the Christian worship —the ignorant savage has been supplanted by the refined European!"

Though mild enough by modern standards—the late 20th century has not been kind to the Victorian Protestant ideal, or to those who strove vigorously to export it— such comments in Melville's time bordered on the scandalous. In fact, this passage was one of the ones cut from the second edition of the book, as being too strong for American audiences.

The Sailor and the Preacher

The natives of the South Seas were not the only targets of the evangelical spirit that fueled Victorian Protestantism. The sailors themselves were frequent objects of missionary attentions both at home and abroad. The American Seaman's Friend Society was founded in 1825. Seeking to turn the sailors from their ways of sin, the Society built churches, reading rooms, and "bethels." The organization distributed bibles and tracts to ships at sea and sponsored prayer sessions aboard when the ships were in port. The New Bedford Port Society was founded in 1830, with the goal of bringing spiritual and moral reform to the sailors.

As men with irregular work habits who roamed from place to place, sailors were viewed with suspicion by the established social order, of which organized religion was the arbiter. Preachers set up their missions in the waterfront areas of San Francisco, Nantucket, and London just as they did on the shores of tropical islands.

Sailors, like the native peoples, were targets of social prejudice, and even among sailors, the whalemen were looked down on as dirty and unskilled. Small wonder, then, that the whalemen in turn looked upon the missionaries with venomous disdain. Knowing that they themselves were good people by their own lights—regardless of what the missionaries said of their way of life—they wondered if the same might be true of the "heathens" whom other missionaries sought to convert.

The End of Eden

The missionaries were not the only source of trouble for the islanders. The "disease and vice" that Melville speaks of were mainly brought to the South Seas by sailors who came ashore on liberty (See next page). Many of the sailors aboard the commercial and naval ships who called at the island ports brought with them sexually transmitted diseases that had been previously unknown in the Pacific. Five sailors from

Melville's *Acushnet* died during the course of their cruise of "disreputable diseases."

Combine this with the casual relationships that took place on the decks of the *Dolly* with the "whihenies," or young women of the islands, ("...Our ship was now wholly given up to every species of riot and debauchery. Not the feeblest barrier was interposed between the unholy passions of the crew and their unlimited gratification....") and a public health disaster for the islanders was well underway.

Yet more trouble came to the South Sea islanders through the desire of the Western powers for the prestige and wealth that came from overseas colonies. In 1842, this trouble arrived at Nuku Hiva in the form of six French warships, already anchored in Taiohae when the *Acushnet* (and her fictional counterpart, the *Dolly*) entered the bay. The French were under the command of Rear Admiral DuPetit-Thouars, who had just claimed the Marquesas islands for King Louis Phillipe of France. The Admiral was using the threat

THE "DOLLY" WAS FAIRLY CAPTURED BY THE FAIR INVADERS, AND NEVER, I WILL SAY, WAS A VESSEL CARRIED BEFORE SUCH A PARTY OF DASHING AND IRRESISTIBLE BOARDERS...

LATER WE LEARNED THAT THE GROUP OF THE ISLANDS HAD JUST BEEN TAKEN POSSESSION OF BY REAR ADMIRAL DU PETIT THOUARS OF THE FRENCH NAVY...

AS WE ADVANCED UP THE BAY, NUMEROUS CANOES PUSHED OFF FROM THE SURROUNDING SHORES, THEIR SAVAGE OCCUPANTS STRUGGLING TO GET ABOARD OF US...

of his ships' guns to coerce the native chiefs into giving up their sovereignty.

At the time Melville jumped ship on Nuku Hiva, the French had not yet sailed into the smaller bay at Taipivai (the valley of the Typees). Their presence in Taiohae, however, was known to Mehevi and the other inhabitants of the valley. The influence of the French squadron upon the events in *Typee*, while not direct, was considerable: Tommo and Toby, because they fear being pursued by sailors off the French ships as well as by the locals, decide to head for the valley of the Happars rather than staying near the shore; and Mehevi's own worries about the "Franee" (as he calls them) probably influenced his treatment of the two deserters.

Herman Melville couldn't have known it at the time, but his brief sojourn in the valley of the Typees took place near the end of the way of life that he witnessed and—perhaps—was tempted for a while to join. Between the destruction of the islands' culture by Western commerce and Western religion, and the reduction of the indigenous population by hunger and disease, the Earthly paradise of the South Seas didn't last out the century.

Study Questions

•In your opinion, is *Typee* a novel, a work of nonfiction, or something else altogether? Does the knowledge that it was Melville's first published work, written while he was still finding his voice as a writer, influence your opinion?

•Do you think that Tommo is an honest narrator? That is, does he report accurately what he sees, or does he have a hidden agenda that colors his remarks and the incidents he chooses to portray?

• How does Tommo come to speak Polynesian so fluently that he can give accurate translations of everything said around him? Did Melville speak Polynesian with the same degree of fluency, or is that one of the fictional elements in the book?

•Do you think that Tommo was justified in jumping ship? Was he then justified in fleeing the Typee? How alike or dissimilar are his two desertions?

• When Herman Melville wrote *Typee*, the settlement of the American West was well underway. Can you draw any parallels between Melville's description of what was happening in the South Pacific, and what was going on at home in America? Do you think that Melville intended any of those parallels?

•Throughout their time among the Typee, and despite what seems like pretty generous and kindly treatment by their hosts, Tommo and Toby continue to expect the worst. Why is it that the hospitality of the Typee does not change Tommo's expectation of danger from his hosts? What do you think of Tommo's behavior as a "guest" of the Typee?

About the Essayist:

Debra Doyle holds a Ph.D. from the University of Pennsylvania, and has taught at Penn, Villanova, and the University of New Hampshire. With her husband James Macdonald, Dr. Doyle is the author of adult and young adult fantasy and science fiction, including the popular Mageworld series.